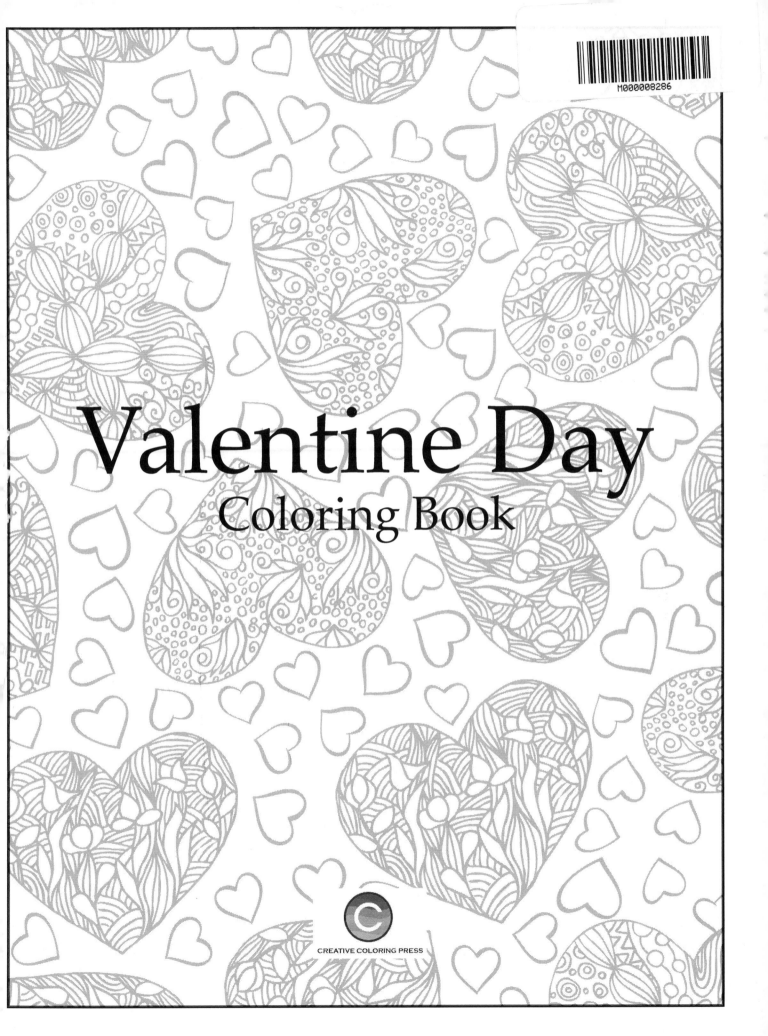

Valentine Day
Coloring Book

CREATIVE COLORING PRESS

This Book

Belongs To

Sign-Up to Get a Free Coloring Book

Subscribe to our newsletter and get a free printable coloring book of some of our most popular illustrations. Plus you'll receive special offers, sneak peeks at new releases, and more. Visit us at www.creativecoloring.co for details.

We hope you've enjoyed this coloring book and that is brings you many hours of fun, stress relief, and creativity. We'd love to see and share your creations.

We want to hear from you!

Send us your ideas, suggestions, and finished artwork:

www.creativecoloring.co
facebook.com/creativecoloringpress
Instagram: @creativecoloringpress
Twitter: @creativecoloringpress

Bonus

Turn the page for bonus pages from some of our most popular coloring books.

DRAGON
COLORING BOOK FOR ADULTS

INCLUDES 38
DAZZLING
DRAGON DESIGNS
TO COLOR

Dragon Coloring Book for Adults by Creative Coloring Press
Available now at Amazon.com, Barnes and Noble, and other online retailers.

Elephant Coloring Book for Adults by Creative Coloring Press
Available now at Amazon.com, Barnes and Noble, and other online retailers.

CREATIVE COLORING PRESS

LIFE UNDER THE
SEA
COLORING BOOK FOR ADULTS

An
Ocean
Coloring
Adventure

Life Under the Sea Coloring Book for Adults by Creative Coloring Press
Available now at Amazon.com, Barnes and Noble, and other online retailers.

CREATIVE COLORING PRESS

COLORFUL HOME

INTERIOR DESIGN COLORING BOOK FOR ADULTS

A COLORING BOOK FOR GROWN-UPS

ALISA CALDER

Colorful Home Interior Design Coloring Book by Alisa Calder.
Available now at Amazon.com, Barnes and Noble, and other online retailers.